8 Steps to GETTING REAL with CANCER

**Empowering Newly-Diagnosed Patients
and Those Who Love Them**

8 Steps to
GETTING REAL
with CANCER

**Empowering Newly-Diagnosed Patients
and Those Who Love Them**

Marianne C. McDonough

Sapphire River Publishing Services, Inc.

Sapphire River Publishing Services, Inc.
250 Prairie Center Drive, Suite 204
Eden Prairie, MN   55344
sapphireriverpublishing@outlook.com

Scriptures taken from:

The Amplified® Bible. Copyright © 1954, 1958, 1962, 1964, 1965, 1987 by The Lockman Foundation. Used by permission. (www.Lockman.org)

ESV® Bible (The Holy Bible, English Standard Version®). Copyright © 2001 by Crossway, a publishing ministry of Good News Publishers. Used by permission. All rights reserved.

The Holy Bible, New International Version®, NIV®. Copyright © 1973, 1978, 1984 by International Bible Society. Used by permission of Zondervan Publishing House. All rights reserved.

The New King James Version®. Copyright © 1982 by Thomas Nelson, Inc. Used by permission. All rights reserved.

Cover stock photography by Steven Arnold/dreamstime.com

ISBN-13: 978-0-9966977-0-5
LCCN: 2015916582

Printed in the United States of America

Contents

Acknowledgments

With humble gratitude and great affection, I thank:

My amazing husband, children, grandchildren and extended families for unwavering love and support. I can't imagine going through any crisis without you, much less the cancer journey. You are my heroes.

Faithful neighbors, churches, and friends for praying hard and caring deeply. You were there when I needed you.

Critique group comrades for providing wisdom and good humor. You are daughters of the King and inspiring faith warriors.

William Backus and Marie Chapian for their 1985 landmark book, *Telling Yourself the Truth.* You are forerunners of wisdom for many grateful readers.

Heart Connexion community for my "breakthrough" in 2007, the "tools" to face cancer, and much-needed prayer support. You are champions of grace.

My oncology center medical staff and personnel for meticulous health care. You are a credit to your profession.

Matt Redman for writing the songs, "10,000 Reasons" and "You Never Let Go." You are an instrument in the hands of our healing God.

Dr. Dennis Hensley, my favorite editor, for astounding expertise and insight. You never fail to encourage my heart and motivate me toward excellence.

I am blessed.

Marianne

Foreword

I had the honor originally to meet Marianne when she invited me to speak for the organization, Great Commission Artists, at its 2014 conference, "Journey of the Heart." My subject was art therapy and the benefits it has for healing. Immediately upon meeting Marianne, I felt a kindred connection; her passion and warmth was radiant, and I felt a sense of calm just being in her presence.

About a year later, Marianne found me once more and, again, blessed me with the honor to read her book that she had written, *8 Steps to Getting Real with Cancer*. As a seasoned art therapist, I had led a cancer survivor art therapy group for five years and still hold this cause very close to my heart. Having first-hand witnessed the devastation, loss, and trauma that cancer can cause, I am well aware how survivors struggle to heal as they find their way out of darkness using tools, such as art, to restore the joy that cancer robbed from them. With that said, healing and recovery from this horrible, life-threatening illness *is* possible.

Marianne has written *8 Steps to Getting Real with Cancer* not only as a guide but also as a light to shine the way for cancer victims who, within the first days of diagnosis, are horrified by what to do and how to do it. Marianne approaches this from a Christian perspective, telling how her faith guided her through her own courageous battle with cancer. I especially love the way she tells her story from a *human being's* perspective, showing that our cancer journey, as well as how we react and respond to it, will not be perfect—and that it's okay. Marianne's thread throughout this book is for cancer victims to be authentic, and to trust God and His plan. She validates that indeed, these things may not come easily for us, and we may fumble, but it's all part of the journey for greater faith.

8 Steps to Getting Real with Cancer debunks myths of cancer and presents the truths. It gives the reader "practical applications during treatment and recovery" that are simple, yet wise. Marianne also provides "survivor attitudes" to utilize as guides for recovery. Most importantly, however, she shares a from-the-heart account of her own cancer journey that is captivating and honest. Marianne never pretends that having cancer is easy, affirming often that she had to trust her faith during this time. The theme of this book is that finding our way out of the darkness and trusting the journey will lead us to more light with God and ourselves, thereby bringing a new-found meaning to the life that we are living.

I would recommend *8 Steps to Getting Real with Cancer* to *all* people struggling with cancer: victims, survivors, caregivers, family members, and health providers. This is an excellent and practical healing resource to utilize during a very difficult journey not only for Christians but for the entire human race.

With prayers in your healing journey,
Katie Kinzer, M.A., ATR, LPCC
Registered Art Therapist/Licensed Professional Clinical Counselor

Introduction

Today I don't have cancer. I'm not sure I can convey how wonderful that is, but I'm going to try.

Like a thief, cancer strikes and attempts to ransack our lives, defying us to stop it. Feeling violated and stunned, we have to face this notorious bully head on, and it's a wrenching process.

Anyone who has had cancer probably remembers the exact day of diagnosis, even the hour, circumstances, and details. For many of us, it is our first introduction to mortality, and initially we feel powerless as a sense of foreboding looms and options seem or might actually be quite limited. Somehow we have to find the courage and means to get our power back, and that's the reason I've written this book. Now that I've fought this enemy myself, I want people to understand, patients and supporters alike, how to be effective, confident, and empowered.

How did I come to this conclusion? On Monday, March 12, 2012, at 9:00 a.m. someone told me, "You have invasive ductal carcinoma," and my world collapsed into a sinkhole. I didn't even know the ground was wet. At the time, I couldn't have articulated what I'm writing today. In retrospect, however, armed with my own hard-earned personal experience, I want to inspire patients to attack cancer with vehement determination.

So what are the keys to empowerment in the cancer battle? Frankly, since I'm not naturally combative, I had to learn one small step at a time. But, because I hated feeling powerless and passionately desired life, I decided to do everything I could to direct my own journey with dignity.

To do that, much to my surprise, I had to ask myself some tough questions and be as authentic as possible in the process. What did I know about cancer and believe to be true about myself as a cancer patient? How would I interact with my family and friends? What was my attitude toward medical professionals and the treatment process? How did I feel about possibly dying? Where was God in all of this? How would I deal with the actual treatment and its inherent stress? Last but not least, did I even have a future ahead of me?

For me, asking those questions required a gut-level evaluation of my belief system far beyond anything I had done before. Thus, the only modus operandi that made sense to me was to "get real" with cancer. The problem is that in a culture saturated with "reality" television, many of us, myself included, are not always too good at being real, especially under pressure. Consequently, I organized the following eight chapters to chronicle the "steps" I took toward this incredibly hard but rewarding goal.

As you read this book, I encourage you to embrace your uniqueness. When your beliefs, personality, religion, upbringing, and life experiences meet at the intersection of cancer and your own life, everything shifts into gear. So be kind to yourself, listen to your heart, never forget how valuable you are, and be as authentic as you can possibly be.

Additionally, please understand that when I present the myths and truths in this book, I am not trying to tell you how to think. Rather my hope is that you will explore and clarify your own beliefs. I am encouraging a process not precepts. You will see that I am a Christian and that my faith is important to me. That's who I am and have been for most of my life; thus, this book reflects my own spiritual struggles, too, especially when I was first diagnosed and later when it was time to get real with my fears.

Finally, I urge you to design and define your own course. You need to do that! No matter the direction or detours, even if you feel lost now and then (I had my moments), you can still discover greater wisdom and healing than you ever thought possible and can even imagine at this point.

You can do this!

Know that, as a survivor, I have faith for you and in you. May your triumphs be many as you experience the combined strength of your true self and our loving God. Moreover, may the days ahead be among the best of your life.

You have my prayers,
Marianne McDonough

CHAPTER ONE

Step #1: Getting Real with Yourself

Cancer Changes You Forever—Make It a Positive Change

What is Getting Real?

In most respects being human is a great adventure, but crises such as cancers, whether our own or someone else's, shake our souls to the core. If ever we need to articulate our beliefs and feelings, it's in the shocking weeks that follow diagnosis.

Prior to 2012, two factors prepared me to embrace "getting real" as a modus operandi during cancer: *Telling Yourself the Truth* by William Backus and Marie Chapian and Heart Connexion Seminars taught by Dr. Paul and Susanna Fitzgerald in Kansas City, Kansas. Thanks to the former, I understood the value of truth in self talk, and thanks to the Fitzgeralds, I learned about being "100% real" via God's grace in context with community. Not that I sailed through cancer treatment without a problem, but my basic mindset knew how to steer a rudder and read the wind.

Here are short lists of what getting real means to me, as well as what it doesn't mean:

Getting real is:

1. Growing in self-awareness of what is true inside of me.
2. Identifying my strengths honestly and my weaknesses compassionately.

3. Seeing myself as a worthy human, created and loved by God.
4. Respecting myself enough to be considerate and expressive of my own feelings and values.
5. Respecting others enough to communicate in non-threatening ways and to give them the freedom to respond accordingly.
6. Making intentional decisions that reflect an honest appraisal of my needs.
7. Giving myself the freedom to pursue and fulfill my God-given purpose.
8. Fostering healthy relationships based on mutually honoring behavior.

Notice that all the verbs end in "ing." I did that deliberately to convey that getting real is an ongoing process.

Getting real is not:

1. Judging or condemning myself or anyone else.
2. Advertising my weaknesses or anyone else's.
3. Disguising negative emotion in word or action.
4. Disrespecting myself with shaming conversation or self-talk.
5. Disrespecting others, directly or indirectly, with shaming conversation or behavior.
6. Trying to control everyone and everything.
7. Considering only my needs at the expense of others.
8. Placing unrealistic expectations on others or myself.

The Beginning of Getting Real with Cancer

In March 2012, the physician's assistant completed my routine physical, giving me the following option: "You don't have to get a mammogram this year, if you don't want to."

> "You don't have to get a mammogram this year,
> if you don't want to."

"Really?" I responded. Not particularly fond of mammograms, I wanted to hear more.

"Yes, you're 65 years old and haven't had any problems thus far. Plus, there isn't any history in your family. You had a mammogram last year, so you could wait until 2013."

"Will Medicare pay for it?"

"Certainly."

"Well," I said, "in that case, I've already made the appointment, so I'll just get one anyway."

When I think about that pivotal decision, I shake my head at what could have happened had I decided to wait.

The mammogram seemed routine, and I was allowed to leave, totally unaware that a small tumor, undetectable by physical examination, lay in my left breast and had already begun to spread. Having had numerous tests before without incident, I didn't give it a second thought.

Until the next day, when they called me back for the ultrasound.

"What does this mean?" I asked.

"Do you want to talk to a nurse?"

"Yes, please."

Calmly the nurse explained that further testing didn't necessarily mean I had cancer but my results warranted another look. Pacing with my hand over my mouth, I felt an odd panic emerge in my gut. Then I decided to get real with her.

"I'm afraid."

She was a stranger, and I didn't know her at all, but I figured I needed to say it, so I did.

As her voice warmed, I felt her compassion. To her credit, she responded with the exact empathy and encouragement I needed.

At first, I only told my husband and children. After all, callbacks frequently prove to be innocuous. But the next day, as soon as the ultrasound technician said, "There it is," I felt a shift in my soul.

If you are a breast cancer patient, you know the drill. The ultrasound led to a biopsy, followed by an agonizing wait period. In my case I had the biopsy late Thursday afternoon, so the results wouldn't be available until Monday. At this point, I began to feel cornered emotionally, and I expanded my circle of confidantes. Repeatedly, I tried to tell myself, "You're fine. It's probably benign. Stop worrying. God's got this. It's nothing."

I changed my mind, however, on Sunday morning when my husband and I went to church.

That morning the worship focused on trusting God in the midst of storms. Appropriate, indeed, but amazingly, our worship leader had chosen two songs in particular that became a mainstay of hope for me. The first was Matt Redman's "10,000 Reasons," and the second, also by Redman, "You Never Let Go," especially the lyric quoting Psalm 23:4, "Even though I walk through the valley of the shadow of death...." (ESV)

God didn't write a message in the sky or hand me a note, but, for the first time, a realization sunk in and settled the matter. I could have cancer. Afterward, knowing that I had to get pains-takingly real with the situation, I went home and prayed all afternoon. At first I tried to think and say all the things a good

Christian should think and say, but I found no peace in that. Finally, with heart-rending clarity, I admitted, "God, I don't feel like a faith giant right now. I'm not sure I can measure up."

Responding to "You Never Let Go," I read Psalm 23. Slowly, I went through each verse, noting that He would lead me in safe paths. But how could cancer's path be safe, especially through the valley of the shadow of death? Adding to my dilemma, I recalled the dear people in my life who died from cancer and how hard they struggled. Would I have to walk that path? Part of me wanted to dismiss the possibility, but what if I had cancer? Wouldn't I want to be somewhat prepared?

I felt vulnerable. Desperately I continued to search Psalm 23. Then one word in particular, the word "shadow" in verse 4, stood out like headlights on a dark road. I was walking through the valley of death's shadow, not death itself. Granted, cancer casts an ominous shadow, but still, a shadow is only a shadow and has no power of its own.

Relaxing, I braced myself for the weeks ahead.

Myth #1: I can't be open and honest with people right now.

Truth #1: I can communicate as much or as little as I want, as long as I do so with clarity and a true sense of what is best for me. The diagnosis period is one of the hardest parts of cancer. By discovering and expressing my real thoughts and needs from the beginning, I facilitate the rest of the journey.

Myth # 2: Emotional expression is a sign of weakness and spiritual immaturity.

9

Truth #2: Emotional expression requires courage and self-respect. I do not have to be ashamed of who I am or how I feel, especially as I begin to grapple with cancer. Spiritual maturity thrives on truth and honesty, not platitudes and pretense.

Getting the News

Even though I thought the worst could happen, I was hoping for the best of the worst, which to me was in situ breast cancer. That would mean it had not spread anywhere. But that's not what happened, and I was shocked.

Monday morning began with my painter and his crew arriving. I had scheduled the work several weeks previously. Since I was uncertain about the pending diagnosis, I kept the painting project on the calendar. Besides, Mike Webster had done a lot of work for me before, and I was comfortable with him in the house.

The phone rang shortly after 9 a.m. Grabbing the receiver; I started to go downstairs to be alone. By the time I reached the second set of stairs, she had already said, "You have invasive ductile carcinoma."

I collapsed at the bottom of the stairs, partially laid out on the lower two steps and partially on the ground floor. I don't even remember my back hitting the stairs. Having flung my left arm straight out to the side, I pressed the phone to my right ear, struggling to catch my breath.

Invasive? Dear God! I alternately squeezed my eyes shut as each breath pressed hard against my chest. They were the kind of breaths you take when you've been under water for a long time and finally reach the surface. I remember her delivery seemed measured and calm, most likely a deliberate strategy to counteract the shock of the diagnosis. To me, however, although this was probably her normal routine and certainly not callous, her voice sounded as though she could have been reading a grocery list rather than what seemed to be my fragile future. After all, as far as I was concerned, my world had just spun into some sort of UFO orbit.

"You will need to have an MRI and see a surgeon to discuss your options, possibly make an appointment with a plastic surgeon who will need to be scheduled as well, and prepare for surgery within the next few weeks. Depending on the staging and your decisions, you may also have chemotherapy and/or radiation."

As I lay at the bottom of the stairs that Monday morning, my fists started to tighten, and I pulled myself up off the floor. Like a boxer, I felt as though I had just climbed through the ropes. Every muscle in my body was tight, and I longed to swing at something, anything. I think I would have beat on the wall had I been alone in the house.

> Like a boxer, I felt as though I had just climbed through the ropes. Every muscle in my body was tight, and I longed to swing at something, anything. I think I would have beat on the wall had I been alone in the house.

In retrospect, I believe that my vigorous soul-searching paid off when the moment of truth arrived. My survival instinct felt raw, real, and surprisingly ready, like a guard dog sensing an intruder. The battle had officially begun.

"Could you come in tomorrow for the surgeon?"

"Yes. I will come in today if you want."

"We can't do it today, but tomorrow afternoon at three o'clock is open."

"Done."

"All right, we'll schedule the MRI for Wednesday then."

"What's the MRI for?"

"It's another diagnostic tool to determine how far the cancer has spread."

"How long does it take to get the results?"

"Usually, we have the results by the next day."

"That doesn't make sense to me. Why don't we do that before I see the surgeon, so he has all the information I need?"

"Well, a doctor has to order it. And you have to have a blood test first."

"Okay. You know I have the cancer. Why can't someone order it?"

"But you have to have a blood test first, and that takes several hours."

"Then I'll go get the blood test right now."

"Just a minute."

As I look back on this conversation, I realize I took control of my process immediately. Why should I sit around and wait for cancer to make the next move? Therein was one of my first lessons. I felt stronger taking action and being assertive.

To her credit, the nurse returned to the phone, having obtained a doctor's order from my OB/GYN, impressively creative on her part. The MRI was on the docket for 6:30 p.m. that night, and we made arrangements for the blood test at a lab nearby at noon.

Just as I ended the call, Mike, the painter, came down the stairs to find me. When he saw my face, he said, "Are you all right?

"No, Mike, I just found out I have breast cancer."

Instantly he gasped but without hesitation said, "My mother beat breast cancer twice, and so can you. I will pray for you."

What a great response! Those words of empowerment darted out of his mouth and straight into my heart. Further conversation revealed that we shared the same faith. I was so grateful for him!

"Do you want us to leave?"

"No, let's just get the project done."

"Okay, but if you want us to go, we can."

"It's all right, Mike. Thanks for offering."

Myth #3: Cancer is a death sentence. I have little, if any, hope for survival.

Truth #3: Cancer is life threatening but no longer the automatic death sentence it once was. Many people survive to live productive and fruitful lives. Look at the masses of people who walk for cancer cures, who volunteer countless hours to help support new patients, who bravely forge into their future to leave a legacy of strength for the rest of us. I will set my heart and soul to beat this disease and live a stronger and more meaningful life as a result.

Myth #4: Cancer will limit my life and my dreams.
Truth #4: Obviously, I cannot look into the future or predict my longevity, but I can still look forward to life. I can choose to take positive action and engage fully in the healing process. Rather than see myself as limited, I can grow as a person, appreciate life as never before, and continue to dream.

Practical Applications

1. Despite the frantic pace of the first few weeks, I will sit down, relax, and get real with myself. I will resist being like a hamster in a wheel, running and spinning to no place in particular.
2. I will be deliberate and communicative.
3. I will give myself permission to fight this disease whole-heartedly.
4. I will get informed. Some of the data are awful to read, but the more I learn about cancer and what lies ahead of me, the more I empower myself.

Survivor Attitude

I will set my heart on a positive course and make a conscious choice to do everything I can to survive. My power, destiny, and future are still in God's hands. He and I can do this together. I can walk through the valley of the shadow of death, knowing that it is only a shadow and that He is at my side.

CHAPTER TWO

Step #2: Getting Real with Your Family
Cancer Shocks Your Family—They Don't Know What to Do

Getting Real with Priority Relationships

Most of us have priority relationships, and I acknowledge that yours may be different from mine, but whatever your situation is, or marital status, family composition, or level of connection with primary relationships, please perceive the principles I am sharing and apply them to your needs.

In this chapter, I will focus on my immediate family, which includes my husband, children, and grandchildren.

Married for 49 years, Tom and I have had many successes as well as hard times together. We are a classic example of opposites attracting, tending to approach almost everything differently. At times, this complicates our lives. When we combine our strengths, however, we're a formidable partnership. Generally, we're both good problem solvers, even though our processes vary quite a bit. But, in most ways, we're just a normal couple who has loved one another through all the joys and challenges of life.

In the case of cancer, the process was mine, and that presented a short-lived issue at first. Tom's a take-charge kind of guy—a self-employed sales representative with a quick wit and a good measure of practicality. I remember almost 50 years ago when we were dating, he told me he dreamed about being my hero, and I'm sure he still feels that way. With his own brand of creativity, he views challenges like a handyman, often devising clever means to fix them as fast as possible. After receiving my diagnosis, I called him, and he had little to say at first, other than he was sorry.

As I began to share what little I knew at that point, understandably, he went into his how-can-I-fix-this-for-you mode and began to brainstorm what he would do, "If it were me, I would..." Ordinarily, a conversation like that would be normal, even helpful, for either one of us; but I was still dealing with the shock of it, so after we hung up, I prayed, "God, I just found out I have cancer. I have to call the kids, get my blood test, and prepare myself for an MRI. Please help Tom know how to work with me on this. I have to move on."

That night, much to my relief, Tom shared that he had called his buddy John, whose wife had been through breast cancer. John had said, "You've got to let her make her own decisions. It's important for her to be able to do that." That sentence helped both Tom and me! John articulated what I was feeling but hadn't consciously recognized yet, and Tom was better prepared to support me.

Surprising myself, I responded, "Tom, if you tell me what you think I should do, and I feel pressured to do it, what if that turns out to be the wrong thing for me? Or worse, disastrous? I don't want that for you or me. Or if I don't do what you think I should do, then we would feel awkward, and that would affect our relationship, and I don't want that either."

After that conversation, from that point forward Tom did well, although I appreciate how hard it was for him to filter what and how much to say. During the next few weeks, as

I grappled with the weighty decisions ahead of me, he listened and talked to me but didn't apply pressure toward any one solution. He also took me out to dinner a lot, which I loved. I am the main cook in the family, so it was helpful not to worry about that; but, more importantly, we enjoyed pleasant opportunities to relax. You see, in order for him to be my hero, he had to encourage me to find the hero in myself.

> You see, in order for him to be my hero,
> he had to encourage me to find the hero in myself.

He couldn't rescue me from the villain or solve the problem for me. Rather, he could love me best by respecting me and trusting that I could fight and win, while he, for his part, would stand at my side and cheer me on.

Simply put, people's significant relationships make a huge difference, especially because of the level of intimacy involved. Uniquely positioned, loved ones can encourage, observe, listen, and find ways to help lift the load of daily tasks. The cancer patient is a unique human being, and, as such, she will bring her own sense of self to the situation. The more she feels honored and valued, the more empowered she will be to tackle the incredibly complicated options that lie before her.

Addressing Family Members

The following is intended for those of you who are family members of cancer patients:

For me, suddenly something ominous had interrupted my life, demanding my attention, changing all my plans. I felt like a teenager taking my first driver's education lesson in a semi-truck. What I needed more than anything was to learn how to navigate my treatment and find the courage to lead the fight. I knew I was entering a war zone, and it was my war. I wanted Tom next to me, but he couldn't take over, solve it, or do it for me. He wasn't the one going into surgery or possible chemotherapy or radiation.

Again, I want to mention that I understand not everyone is married or has a good marriage. I get that. But my purpose here is to share my experience such that readers may transfer the basic principle of the story, which, in this instance, involves the emotional support and input of significant others in our lives.

When it was all said and done, I was proud of my husband, and I believe the feeling was mutual. We were heroes together, but in different ways.

Myth #5: I have to take my family members' advice or their feelings will be hurt.

Truth #5: I choose to take the helm and make my own decisions. The greatest blessing my family members can give me is to believe in me.

Getting Real with My Children

For forty-plus years I've had the honor and pleasure of mothering two extraordinary women. I've never known anyone else in my life, other than my sister, for whom I've had so much respect. They are beautiful human beings, capable, smart, and deeply spiritual.

I hated telling them I had cancer. It pained me to the core. All I've ever wanted for them is to be happy, and with such awful news I certainly would bring them sorrow. Although confident that they would do anything they could for me, I was angry that this thing called cancer had intruded into my life and now theirs like a bear into a tent of unsuspecting campers.

> Although confident that they would do anything they could for me, I was angry that this thing called cancer had intruded into my life and now theirs like a bear into a tent of unsuspecting campers.

Their shock was palpable, even over the phone. Grief shook through their voices, and I could practically hear their tears. Part of me wanted to pour out to them, because they're my friends, but another part of me wanted to protect them, because they're my children. Neither one said much, asking a few questions and mostly listening. Even my younger daughter, Shannon, who's an accomplished litigator and makes her living as an advisor, simply expressed her sorrow. My older daughter, Sheila, a mother of three and a nursing student at the time, did the same. Both daughters let me know in no uncertain terms that they would be there for me and help in any way possible.

I cried. Not on the phone, but afterward. It was one of the hardest parts of my cancer journey.

Thereafter, Sheila had the sad task of telling her three gorgeous daughters—Lauren, Natalie, and Daisy—ages 12, 10, and 7 years old at the time. All three girls have a deep faith in

Christ, as does their mom, who led them in prayer. The thought of my grandchildren dealing with their grandmother having cancer saddened me, but I know they were and continue to be valiant in my behalf.

At this point I want to extend special recognition and empathy to parents of cancer patients. I pray this book will comfort and encourage you as well.

Through times such as cancer, the crisis moments in our lives, we understand the value of family. God's design for connecting us that way is infinitely brilliant. If, however, you are estranged in some way from your parents, children, siblings or other extended family members, you don't have to go through this alone. I hope you have people in your life who are like family to you, or at least upon whom you can call for support at this difficult time.

In the final analysis, everyone involved has to be honest, sometimes painfully so, because cancer is tedious, and there's nothing simple or easy about it. But, more importantly, honesty unites the troops for the battles ahead.

Myth #6: I have to protect my family, especially my children.

Truth #6: I did not invite cancer to invade my life, and I would love to spare my family this trauma. Realistically, however, I don't have that option.

Family Kicking into Gear

On the way to my first appointment with the surgeon, Tom drove, Shannon accompanied us in the back, and I drew some deep breaths in the front passenger seat. Sheila would have come, but she lived too far away to accompany us in the beginning. "Darn," I said, "I forgot my recorder. I was going to tape things so I could listen later."

"You don't need that, Marianne," Tom responded. "You have Shannon."

Notebook in hand, she sat ready and smiling behind me. Always an excellent student, Shannon definitely knew how to take notes. She didn't miss a thing, went back to the office, and typed her notes for me. What a gift! I referred to those notes often, and I still have them.

She also consulted medical experts whom she knew from her practice and transcribed those notes as well. Day after day, whether with me physically or not, she never left my side emotionally. Anyone who has a litigator in the family will understand how amazing the following statement is: Shannon came to all of my appointments except one, and only because that was a last-minute change.

Even though I knew she chose to help, one morning I began to feel guilty, thinking about the monumental effort she was making despite the demands of her profession. That night, in an effort not to "bother her," I didn't share everything that was on my mind. With her usual keen discernment, she asked me what was wrong. I got real with her and explained that I felt bad about taking up so much of her time. In return, she got real with me. "Mom, please don't leave me out of this. Talk to me. Tell me anything. I want to be a part of your process. I want to do this." After that interchange, I didn't hold back anything. I felt better, though, for giving her the option to set boundaries as possibly needed.

My other daughter, Sheila, was frustrated about not being able to help, saying, "I just want to get there and hug you." At first, she wanted to come from Missouri right away, but as much as I would have loved that, after considering her busy schedule and travel distance (about ten hours), I asked her to come for the surgery instead. Did I want Sheila there from the start? Of course, but circumstances precluded her ability to do so. Even though I couldn't wait to see her, I knew the surgery days were the best option and most helpful to me.

I also thought, recalling her computer savvy and artistic bent, that Sheila was the perfect person to set up a website for me. She did an excellent job, and the end result was that I felt as though she was with me in spirit, as evidenced by her first journal entry:

03/18/12 , 11:57AM

"Hello, friends and family. Here we begin a challenging journey of hope and healing, hand in hand with my mom, Marianne, who was diagnosed with breast cancer this week. We found out the devastating news that she has invasive ductal carcinoma last Monday, March 12. Monday was a very hard day for my mom and our family.

Each day this last week has brought us new information about Mom's specific medical situation and a disease we didn't expect to be studying at this time in our lives. We did receive good news on Tuesday, that it is likely that this tumor was caught early, and it does not appear to have spread to the lymph nodes (we won't know for sure on that until they biopsy the lymph nodes during surgery). Therefore, based on information thus far, we are hopeful that this cancer will be classified as stage I. We are encouraged by this news, which gives us great hope.

Mom has surgery scheduled for Wednesday, March 28, at Methodist Hospital in St. Louis Park, MN. She has been given a lot of information and is reviewing her options for surgery and treatment. Please pray that God will help her make these important decisions and also that He will guide every medical professional to take the best possible care of her.

We hope to use this website to connect all of the people who love my mom and want to be closely involved in this process. Thank you for the outpouring of support and prayers you all have already extended to my mom and our family. We cherish your prayers and we are trusting God right now for healing, strength, and courage.

I love you so much, Mom.

Sheila"

Myth #7: I don't want to be a burden to my family.

Truth #7: When I trust family members to participate in my cancer journey, I express my confidence in them and their love. If I leave them out, I risk hurting them and denying myself the strength of their support. We can communicate about how they can best help, considering circumstances and schedules. Then they are free to stand with me on their own terms, and we all will benefit.

Practical Applications

1. From the point of diagnosis and throughout, I can and must make my own decisions, but that does not mean I have to function in isolation. To the contrary, my family's support helps strengthen and empower me.

2. For the decision-making process, I will have to gather a myriad of information. My family needs to become informed as well. Thus, conversations among us can be enlightening for all.
3. I can ask for and receive help when I need it.
4. Geographical separation doesn't preclude involvement, especially with the incredible technological tools now available.
5. In the final analysis, my treatment plan and all sundry details are my responsibility.

Survivor Attitude

Crises such as cancer remind us of how important our primary relationships are. Whether with spouses, children, siblings, or people who are like family to us, our relationships are fundamental to the cancer journey. I will invite my loved ones to share my journey, and, in return, receive the blessing of their companionship.

In any case, I do not have to travel this path alone. I am valuable and my life is worthy of support.

CHAPTER THREE

Step #3: Getting Real with Your Medical Providers

Cancer Doesn't Play Fair—Choose Your Strategies Wisely

False Expectations

Does anyone go through life without disappointments? I don't think so. You've probably had your share, and so have I. Expectations, like trees in a forest, come in all sizes and shapes: short, tall, thick, and thin. If rooted in truth and reality, they provide protection and shade, but, if not, they can collapse in a storm, obstructing our path or, worse, crushing us beneath their weight.

Little by little during my cancer journey, false expectations toppled before me. I had to identify and remove them, especially those that affected my medical care.

For me, negative expectations seeded my soul at a very young age. My parents were good people but not emotionally healthy in some ways. I won't go into how that all worked, but suffice it to say that I ended up thinking I had to be perfect to be acceptable. Sadly, I certainly am not alone in this regard. Lots of people believe things like: "I have to be the perfect child or student, the perfect spouse or parent, the perfect employee or employer, the perfect friend or neighbor, the perfect leader, or the perfect Christian. I can't ever make a mistake, even a small one."

Unfortunately, as a cancer patient, this translates to, "I have to be a perfect patient." Often we give or hear compliments such as "Wow! So and so is such a champ! She's sure handling it well" or "He has such a great attitude" or "She never complains and always has a smile on her face."

Really? That's some kind of forest to navigate when it happens to you. Although generally happy, I didn't smile all the time before cancer, much less during it, especially at the beginning when decisions barraged my stunned brain for about three weeks.

The reality? I've never met any human who's perfect at anything, even people I've greatly admired. Most of us paddle our canoes one stroke at a time, with varying degrees of proficiency through all the stormy rivers of life. Although I try to be good to people, my cancer choices were not about cordiality or winning a popularity contest at the hospital. Rather, my task was to find the real Marianne and give her permission to communicate authentically, even if she didn't get the "Perfect Patient of the Year" award.

> Although I try to be good to people, my cancer choices were not about cordiality or winning a popularity contest at the hospital. Rather, my task was to find the real Marianne and give her permission to communicate authentically, even if she didn't win the "Perfect Patient of the Year" award.

Myth #8: I have to be the perfect patient.

Truth #8: I choose to be an honest patient. This process is not about making the doctors and nurses like me. It's about creating the best treatment plan possible for my diagnosis.

Meeting the Team

Fortunately, my first doctor's appointment with my surgeon provided a stellar example of what good patient rapport looks like. I hope doctors read this book for this paragraph, if nothing else because, from the time this wonderful man walked in the room to when he left, he never squirmed, or looked at his watch, or gave me any indication that I was imposing on his busy schedule. Rather, his demeanor was calm, and once he sat, he gave us the impression he would stay there as long as we needed. Throughout the subsequent hour, he listened and invited questions, all the while maintaining eye contact primarily with me. Not that he left Tom and Shannon out, but he focused his eyes on mine and seemed intent that I understood everything. I felt confident he cared and would do a fabulous job for me.

For that reason I congratulate the nurse who scheduled my appointments. She really nailed that one. As the go-between for my care, she was the one who informed me of my diagnosis and managed to expedite the initial MRI. As nice as she was, however, she and I had a few shaky moments. Unlike the surgeon, she did not have a communication style that worked well with me. Thus, we did not always connect effectively, in either direction, although we both tried. I have a detailed mind and ask a lot of questions with subsequent follow-up questions, probably the journalist in me. She liked to keep things short and concise. Whatever the reason, I grew increasingly frustrated.

For my part, I was reading everything I could find: studying, taking notes, studying some more. It seemed to me that the more I learned, the more capable I felt. Armed with information, I was equipping myself to fully engage in treatment.

Finally, one day during the second week, I became exasperated. After a considerable period of rephrasing my questions in multiple ways, I told her I didn't know what to do. As respectfully as I could muster, I said, "I know you're trying and you're obviously a knowledgeable person, but I don't feel as though we're understanding each other. I'm sorry. I'm done." She apologized, too, and we said good-bye. Then I sat in my kitchen and vented out loud with a mixture of ranting frustration and prayer. I don't recall exactly what I said, but it's probably just as well because it wasn't pretty. In the end, I asked God to help.

The next day she called me back, having arranged for me to meet with an oncologist the following morning, Friday, at 8:00. Usually, at our clinic, patients don't consult their oncologists until after surgery, but she changed the protocol to help me. On Friday, much to my relief, my oncologist answered every question completely. Then I found out it was her day off, and she had come in especially and only for me. She told me that the nurse had said, "Maybe you can answer all her questions." Impressed, I gave the scheduling nurse credit for persevering until she found a solution. Thanks to both her and the oncologist, I moved forward with confidence.

Please think about that story. My oncologist, a busy doctor with a young daughter at the time, came in on her day off to help me. Truly admirable, in my opinion! Tom described her by saying, "She is obviously a scientist and communicates facts well." We both liked her, and I knew I had another winner on my team. Unfortunately, she has relocated since my treatment, disappointing for me at first, but I am equally happy with my new oncologist.

Before leaving this subject, I want to add how important it is to accommodate your own personality and modus operandi during the various tasks of cancer. For me, cancer required heart and head energy. Personally, in my everyday world, I enjoy both processes. I like using my head in all the practical ways that enable me to be sensible in life, and I enjoy learning, but as an artistic type of person, I also love to engage my spirit and emotions for creativity and spontaneity. The dilemma is not whether to choose one or the other. Rather, the dilemma is developing the wisdom to coordinate the two, discerning what to do when and operating as a whole and healthy human being. During cancer treatment, my head contributed the analyses I needed, while my heart enabled me to get real, discover my inner truth, and motivate action.

That said, I acknowledge that some of you may not want to know all of the details about your treatment, not because you aren't intelligent, but because you're concerned "TMI" could increase anxiety and make treatment more difficult. That's okay. Be who you are. You can do beautifully with your own definition of the basics you need, as long as you have enough information to feel confident about your treatment decisions.

> Be who you are. You can do beautifully with your own definition of the basics you need, as long as you have enough information to feel confident about your treatment decisions.

As for me, particularly in the first few weeks, I determined to gather as much information as possible because I had no prior breast cancer education. In fact, during this period, I had two dreams reflecting my concerns. In one dream, I attended a college class only to discover that I hadn't studied for a big test because I didn't know it was scheduled. I was asking for an extension when I woke up. In the second dream I was at a conference with no information packet, and I didn't know where to go. That one woke me up as well. Obviously, I needed to study my options in order to feel competent and make decisions.

As a result, each time I met with my medical team, I had done "my homework" before each appointment. I found that helpful, not only for the purpose of asking questions but also for being able to understand the answers. My oncologist commended my proactive approach and viewed it as healthy and a good indication of how I would progress.

> *Myth #9:* Medical care is something I receive. I am helpless, vulnerable, and totally dependent.
>
> *Truth #9:* Medical care is a gift and a responsibility. I can be both grateful and assertive for my care. One attitude does not preclude the other. In fact, gratitude and self-care complement one another well in the cancer journey.

It's Not Easy Speaking Up

As much as I appreciate my clinic, I had some minor concerns to address along the way, and I think that's all right. After all, it would not be fair to expect them to be perfect either. For example, generally doctors use germicide on their hands, but some might do so at the entrance of the examination rooms. I was not aware of that. Thus, when one doctor began to examine my breasts without washing his hands, I noticed and asked him about it. Obviously surprised but not offended, he explained that he had used germicide prior to entering and politely accommodated me.

Hoping to encourage, perhaps even embolden you, I ask you to listen to your heart every step of the way. If you feel at all uncomfortable or have reservations about any aspect of your medical care, give your doctor a chance to explain, establish, or reestablish your comfort level.

Unfortunately, for one part of my care, radiation, I respectfully requested a different radiation oncologist. Although he seemed like a nice person and well-qualified, our communication styles didn't seem to match, and I knew I would be seeing him weekly during the seven-week treatment regimen. Admittedly, changing doctors was awkward, but this was cancer, and I was determined to follow my instincts for what was best for me. Simply put, I just wanted to see if someone else might be a better fit.

This was one of the few times in my life that I was totally unwilling to compromise my preferences and needs. If that's something you struggle with as well, please remember that you have a right and a responsibility to approve your treatment plans, and that includes with whom you work.

Perfect patient? No way, nor did I aspire to be that. Perfect doctors? Just as unrealistic and, I might add, unfair. But in the end, I believe that my hard work paid off, and I had acquired an outstanding medical team that complemented my own modus operandi well. Having participated in and prepared for my process to the best of my ability, I felt grateful for the level of expertise I received.

From the onset I realized that I had to take the lead in advocating for myself. By getting real, I honored my own person and value. After all, the stakes are too high and life is too precious to waste time trying to be perfect. Actually, when I think about it, that goal could actually sabotage the cancer journey. We might think it helps, but instead, as the whole scenario unfolds, we could find that it hinders our process.

Finally, regarding, "She always has a smile on her face," the platitude I mentioned earlier in this section, I think I smiled more as a result of getting real. Maybe not all the time, but a lot, all things considered.

Myth #10: I can't disagree with the doctors/nurses or speak up if I feel strongly about something.

Truth #10: I have a right to be heard. By speaking up I convey my concerns and advocate for my own health. Additionally, I may obtain information to help me feel more confident and knowledgeable about my condition and/or treatment. The medical providers and I have the same goal—saving my life. But if we are not communicating well together, it is my responsibility to persevere until all my questions and concerns have been addressed.

Practical Applications

1. I will do my homework before I meet my doctors so that I am ready to comprehend and inquire.
2. I will assess my personality and needs to select the best approach for working with my medical team.

3. If I have questions or concerns, I will express them honestly until I am satisfied with the answers and/or solutions.

Survivor Attitude

I cannot expect perfection from the medical team or myself, but I can clearly communicate in such a way that we can work well together toward our common goal. I will respect the medical professionals and give them credit for their expertise. Concurrently, I will respect and give myself just as much credit for my own value. I will combine those factors with God's guidance to acquire the best possible outcome. I will speak up for myself, ask questions, express concerns, and communicate until I am satisfied.

CHAPTER FOUR

Step #4: Getting Real with Your Support System

Cancer Can Isolate You or Bring You Closer to People—
It's Your Choice

Learn from Example

I have a hero in the cancer warriors' world. His name is Mike Lubratovich.

At first, I didn't want to include people in this book who have died, but I have to tell you about Mike, because he influenced me greatly. In fact, it was he whose example inspired me to write this book.

Mike was a neighbor. He developed bile duct cancer and fought valiantly for three years. Never pretending it was easy, he shared honestly in an open-hearted way that seemed effortless but brought us into his world and made us feel a part of his life, a part of him. We knew he valued our interest as he conversed easily and without hesitation.

What I loved about him was the way he included all neighbors who inquired, even people who didn't necessarily know him well. Although we're a small association and a close-knit neighborhood, some of us see each other more frequently, but Mike was nice to everyone, and he always answered "How are you doing, Mike?" with a friendly response.

Certainly, some of that was personality, of which he had plenty. But it was more than that. I think Mike was truly comfortable in his own skin. If he hurt, he said so. If he was discouraged, he admitted it. I never saw him minimize his situation with a Pollyanna-kind of pretense. Consequently, when he conveyed good news, we could rejoice, because we knew it was the truth.

He also had a Caring Bridge website. Anyone who didn't really know him before cancer grew to know him better, and, as a result, all of us will never forget him.

Mike died on a Christmas morning. I asked his wife Renee if that was a hard day for it to happen. She brightened and smiled (she has a gorgeous smile!) and said, "Not at all, because I will never be alone on the anniversary of his death. I'll always have family with me." She said Mike passed peacefully and even smiled.

In contrast, years ago a friend expressed her sadness about a co-worker whom she greatly admired. He was a friendly person, she said, and well-respected, but from the onset of cancer, he chose to isolate himself, despite the efforts of friends and family who offered to support. Obviously, he had a right to choose how he would go through cancer and spend his last days, and I, as a survivor, defend his autonomy to make those decisions. My point is, however, that those who cared about him were perplexed and felt awkward at his funeral which was held in another city.

Mike's funeral, conversely, was well attended, full of life, faith, humor, and lots of great stories. We shared a sense of cohesiveness—a genuine gratitude for him and his life. The service was beautiful, and many of his neighbors attended gladly. I was happy for Renee and his family to have so many people there who loved them and him.

As you know from chapter one, when I was called back for my mammogram and went through the subsequent ultrasound and biopsy, I had to wait during the weekend for the results. In the meantime I shared my concern only with my family, a few close friends, and my critique group with whom I had met on Friday morning. I wanted the prayer and emotional support, but, because I had no idea if it was really cancer, I didn't share any further than that.

In the back of my mind, however, because of my neighbor Mike, I knew that if the worst scenario materialized, I would share my heart. I didn't have it all figured out, but I was ready to get real from the start. Then, as I stood stunned at the bottom of my stairs on Monday morning, I had no problem saying to my painter, "I just found out I have breast cancer."

What if I hadn't shared that with him? Suppose I had dismissed him and politely indicated I needed to be alone?

Surely, I could make a case for that, but I would have missed the gift he was to me. As his faith sprang into action, he spoke the exact words I needed. In fact, his response still inspires me, even to this day. "Marianne, my mother beat breast cancer twice, and so can you. I will pray for you." Think about God's timing in all of this. Within seconds of learning I had cancer, this faith-filled young man came downstairs to ask me a question about the painting job, unaware that God chose him to be the first person on my support team.

> Think about God's timing in all of this. Within seconds of learning I had cancer, this faith-filled young man came downstairs to ask me a question about the painting job, unaware that God chose him to be the first person on my support team.

Interestingly, my painter's name is Mike.

Myth #11: People don't want to hear about my woes.

Truth #11: When I confide in people, I open the door for support. They don't have to know every detail, but I can welcome their caring and choose how much, when, and by what means I keep them informed in a way that is comfortable and helpful to them and me.

Myth #12: I don't want to impose on anyone.

Truth #12: People like to help if they can, but they don't always know what to do. I can provide means for them via my family or technology to check up on me and possibly help. I will benefit, and they will be invaluable to my process. My family and I can also set boundaries when necessary. People want to support in ways that are genuinely appreciated.

The Benefits of a Support Team

For those of you who are privileged to be on someone's support team, this next section is for you. I would love to mention everyone by name who reached out to me. But space precludes that, and hoping to inspire you with ideas and examples, I've narrowed my list into generalized categories with a few descriptions:

  * Physical company, conversation, kind deeds:

My amazing sister, Nancy Mitchell, lives in Kansas. When she asked about the best time to come and help, I was thrilled and suggested she arrive post-surgery after my daughter, Sheila, left. Nancy and I are good friends, so we did a lot of sisterly gabbing, but she also made dinners and froze individual portions for subsequent evenings. What a gift! She continues to bless me to this day with her prayers.

As I recovered, I also greatly appreciated my neighbors and friends who brought flowers, shared food, and supplied transportation to radiation appointments.

* Website posts on MyLifeLine.org:

Sheila's hard work getting the website up reaped many benefits. I checked it often, and I assure you that all entries inspired me, no matter the length. Sheila and Shannon alternately wrote updates, and I did a few as well. One fringe benefit was that people who didn't know my children personally came to know them via the updates.

* Prayers:

I believe in prayer. I can't imagine going through cancer without it. Please let the cancer patient know you're praying. Don't worry about being redundant. I never tired of hearing or reading the words, "I'm praying for you." Both my churches (at home and cabin) as well as church friends offered prayer for me, as did relatives, neighbors, social and ministry friends, writing comrades, and even my children's friends.

The MyLifeLine website provides a calendar you can use however you like. I decided to make it a prayer calendar for the weeks during my radiation. My daily appointment was at 10:20 a.m., and to my relief, the calendar filled. Some people like my niece Stefanie Carnes and Tom's niece Anne Buttolph, signed up for multiple days, even certain days on a weekly basis. I thought that was extraordinary.

* Prayer shawls:

During my treatment, I received two beautiful prayer shawls, both of which I still enjoy. As I wrapped the garments around my shoulders, I found it humbling that anyone would take that kind of time for me.

On the Saturday after my surgery, one of my artist friends, Bobbie Sawyer, brought a prayer shawl to me that her church group had made. When she arrived, we were both delighted, because the colors in the shawl exactly matched the blouse I was wearing, and I mean exactly. Bobbie had also prepared a card explaining the significance of the green, purple, and royal blue colors. I decided to bring that shawl with me to radiation, and, to my surprise, the green in the shawl matched the green robe I had to wear.

My neighbor, Audrienne Vidmar, made my other prayer shawl—a comfy, soft, forest-green shawl. I had no idea she knitted, but when she looked at me with those expressive brown eyes and said, "I'm praying for you," I knew I had another powerful ally in my journey. I wore her shawl every day for my morning coffee and quiet times, something I often do four years later, thankfully remembering Audrienne.

> Thanks to today's technology, even if you live far away, you can do a lot to support someone.

* Creative actions and support from long distance relatives and friends:

Thanks to today's technology, even if you live far away, you can do a lot to support someone. My late sister-in-law, Rita Fischbach, who lived in Illinois, was a great encourager when I was going through treatment. Rita's emails, photos, and website posts were steady and numerous. One of her daughters, Carol Clavadetscher, helped her children make a wonderful banner for me. Then she took a photo and posted it on the website.

Rita's other daughter, Anne Buttolph, who is a nurse, and her husband Tom, a pathologist, spent a lot of time one evening explaining things to us via a conference call. Their expertise and insights helped us wade through all the data.

My cousin, Sharon Atcheson, who lives in Tulsa, Oklahoma, went to a cancer support event and lit a candle in my honor, thereafter sending a photo to me. When I received it, I was so touched by her effort and love, I could hardly speak.

* Small gifts:
Though unnecessary, small gifts such as books are lovely. A dear friend, Ann Bojdak, from New York sent me a book called *A Reason For Hope,* that inspired me with one quote in particular, "Hope is hearing the melody of the future. Faith is being able to dance to it." As a dancer, I loved the thought of dancing to the melody of my future.

One tip about books: During the first few weeks, I had so much research to read and assimilate that I did not have time for large books. That is the reason I kept this one as short as possible.

Barb Howe, representing my critique group friends, gave me a plaque that still rests on my porch window sill and reminds me of their support and prayers.

One of my ministry friends, Tammy Sorenson, a powerful and talented worship artist, gave me her most recent CD, a soothing compilation of original music composed to impart healing and peace.

* Greeting cards—any kind, any time:
I'm referring to the kind of cards I could hold in my hand and display on my kitchen shelf. I loved the cards! Whenever I got one, I felt my heart brighten, especially enjoying a handwritten message of any length. Email and ecards were fun, too, but I saw the greeting cards every time I walked in and out of the kitchen. I still have all of them.

My grandchildren made their own cards for me. Is there anything a grandmother loves more? Again, the gift of time means a lot, and their caring came through their artwork and words. I don't even know how many times I picked up those cards and enjoyed them.

* Food and treats:

Yes, the Pillsbury advertisement, "Nothin' says lovin' like something from the oven" is true. Here is an entry I wrote one day after two of my neighbors shared their culinary talents:

> "Tuesday was a good day. At 5:00 my neighbor Judy Smith showed up at my door bearing a lovely plate of lemon bars topped with almonds and coconut. I was on the phone with my sister and commented that one of those bars would make a perfect appetizer for dinner. Nancy, being the supportive person she is, said something like, "Of course, Marianne, you absolutely should do that. You deserve it. Go ahead, dear. What's one dessert bar before dinner?" Okay, she didn't actually say that. I think it was more like, "Go for it!" But by then I had already eaten half of one. Three bars later, dear Rosemary Prohofsky brought us a scrumptious lasagna dinner, complete with Jell-O salad, green beans, and last, but certainly not least, a yummy, moist lemon cake with whipped cream. Did I eat all of that? Of course! And I relished every delicious morsel."

Myth #13: I don't want to bother the cancer patient, so it's better to do nothing.

Truth #13: It's true that cancer treatment is hard work, but I may be able to help in such a way that the patient can focus her energy on the arduous process of healing. I can try to find a family member or close friend to ask what is needed. I can also be creative and do something special right where I am, such as attending a breast cancer event. Last, but not least, I can pray from any location.

Practical applications for the Cancer Patient

1. I will carefully assess how to involve other people in my process.
2. I will determine how to keep them informed in a way that is comfortable and helpful to them and me.

Practical Applications for the Support Team

1. I will pray.
2. I will reach out to the family or friends to learn how I can best support.
3. I will be creative, remembering that the gift of time to go to a cancer walk, send a card, or make a meal contributes in practical as well as emotional ways.
4. I will not let geographical distance deter me. I can do something special right where I am.

Survivor Attitude

I will initiate and keep the lines of communication open to my support system. Considering my personality and circumstances, I will intentionally choose the best way to involve my supporters. I will design a communication framework within which that can best happen.

CHAPTER 5

Step #5: Getting Real with God

Cancer Makes You Face Mortality—Get Clarity in Prayer

Confronting the Fear of Death

Everyone experiences fear, but some fears are harder than others to identify. Sometimes fear protects us from danger, and other times it endangers us. In any scenario fear can activate us or bring us to a standstill, but when it comes to cancer, standing still is not an option.

At first, even though I found the wherewithal to say, "I'm afraid" after the mammogram, I did not equate that emotion with an unconscious fear of death. Eventually, though, I unmasked that specific fear, and it wasn't easy.

For me, mortality had never invaded my mental radar before, and I had to get real with God to track it. Fear of death could sabotage my hope. Proverbs 13:12 says, "Hope deferred makes the heart sick, but a longing fulfilled is a tree of life."(NIV) Since hope and fear are both rooted in the future, my task was to decide which attitude to nurture.

> Since hope and fear are both rooted in the future, my task was to decide which attitude to nurture.

For the first couple of weeks, I didn't dwell on the fear piece, because the immediate crisis consumed my time and energy. I wrote on my cancer support blog:

"Two weeks ago, everything in my life shifted gears.
The Great Commission Artists conference on March 3rd
had turned out beautifully. I was getting the Waterfalls
seminar underway, writing a magazine article due
in April, editing my banners manual, revising my
websites, and finishing a couple of more DVDs. All of
you know how I operate with a variety of projects.

Then a routine mammogram on March 6th propelled
me into a totally unexpected path. On March 12th,
I was waiting for biopsy results from the previous
Thursday. Truthfully, I was sensing it might be bad, but I
was hoping, at least, that it wasn't invasive.

But it was, and here we are...

Clinically, research clearly indicates equal survival rates
for the two alternatives available to me, mastectomy
or lumpectomy plus radiation. Regarding either one, I
have faith for God's power to intervene such that I can
have the best scenario, but I must take a good look at
all the pertinent facts to make an informed choice."

Did you catch the part about "survival rates?" Did you notice how I neatly inserted that phrase into the flow? Or how easily it seemed to fit into the narration?

As I deliberated about options, my brain played ping-pong with the data, landing them on both sides of the net and all over the table.

Finally, after days of pondering, I sat with God and got real with Him on a Saturday morning. Coffee mug steaming, porch all bright and cozy, I situated myself for my favorite time of day. My prayer agenda included the decisions that had to be declared no later than Monday.

At that point I had worked hard to come to "an informed decision." But, despite the swarms of data lodged in my brain, I remained undecided, lacking conviction one way or the other.

As I began, I told God how complicated it all seemed—neither choice was clearly superior. I had chewed on the facts like a piece of tough meat but couldn't get them to the point of swallowing. On the website, I had described it:

"One alternative is a lumpectomy, the easier surgery followed by a seven-week, Monday through Friday, mandatory radiation process that can affect the lung and heart beneath the left breast. From a purely logical viewpoint, that's a risk I need to evaluate. Additionally potential skin issues and a general fatigue can inhibit normal functioning during the treatment and perhaps thereafter for a period of time.

The other, of course, is a mastectomy, a much more difficult surgery with greater risks of infection, a longer recovery period, and possible adverse effects on upper body muscle strength and flexibility. Reconstruction, generally initiated at the mastectomy, involves six to eight subsequent procedures and one to two surgeries in the next nine months as well as replacement surgery in about ten years. In its favor, a mastectomy intuitively seems to offer more closure to the cancer, even though statistics rank it equal to lumpectomy plus radiation."

As I re-examined my options that morning, I realized that, despite the intellectual handle I had acquired, I was at a four-way stop with no clear right of way. It was time to engage my spirit and find my heart.

Then I recalled something a wise Christian woman had shared about her hysterectomy. She said, "I wish I hadn't made my decision based on fear."

Fear, I thought. *Hmmm. I'll just write down any fears I might have.*

Grabbing a pen and pad, I began to write. Surprisingly, I composed a rather long list ranging from "making a mistake" and "pain" to the one that finally caused me to sit back and sigh. Undetected before, the word "death" seemed like a flashing marquis to me. Death? I knew I hated mistakes, and I've never been too good at pain, but death?

For a few minutes I argued with myself. *Come on, now. You believe in heaven. You know you're saved. How could you be afraid of dying? Surely not.* But the sense that I had hit a core issue finally won out, and I let my heart feel the emotion. "God," I said, "I'm sorry to say this to you because I know better spiritually, but I'm scared...I'm not ready to die."

> For a few minutes I argued with myself. *Come on, now. You believe in heaven. You know you're saved. How could you be afraid of dying? Surely not.*

Suddenly, I allowed myself to emote long and hard, spilling out my inmost thoughts, unfiltered and raw: I had unfulfilled dreams, a beautiful family I hated to leave, books to write, ministry goals to pursue, and exciting visions to chase.

But that wasn't the end of it. I talked about my parents and their deaths. How hard it was to watch my father suffer without any morphine, even though his doctor had promised to spare him as much pain as possible. How my mother emitted terrified groans until my sister assured her of God's love and I followed with, "Mom, you're about to go to the other side and meet God face to face. Please pray with me to give your life to Him." After we prayed together, I was relieved to see her relax, and she seemed more peaceful.

Finally, while thinking about death, I also felt concern for my all my loved ones. What would it be like to say "good-bye" to them?

I got real with God.

Myth #14: I have to tell God what He wants to hear so that He will accept me.

Truth #14: God already knows my inner thoughts. Why bother putting on a false face with Him? God is not going to be shocked or dismayed by my honesty. He accepts and loves me unconditionally.

Making Friends with My Own Mortality

Death scared me. I admitted it, but I didn't have a problem believing in eternity, heaven or salvation. Why had I not identified that fear before? The answer was simple. I hadn't had cancer or a reasonable facsimile before.

Was there shame in that moment? No, actually quite the opposite. God was helping me, and I could feel His compassion. He's not in the shame business.

> God was helping me, and I could feel His compassion.
> He's not in the shame business.

I wasn't being a bad Christian, just a normal human one with legitimate concerns. As it turned out, I released all my fears into God's hands and made friends with my own mortality, but it wouldn't have happened without getting real.

After that, my decisions were easier to make. Fear had lost its grip on me. Freely choosing my treatment plan based on data, logic, and my best wisdom at the time, I was empowered for the next phase of my journey.

Myth # 15: A spiritual person, especially a believing Christian, is not afraid, especially of death.

Truth # 15: I am a spiritual person, but I am also human with emotions and an accumulation of experiences lodged in my subconscious. With God's help, I can acknowledge my fears and accept mortality, thus becoming a stronger Christian.

How We See God

Closely linked to all these issues is our concept of God and His interaction with our lives. With cancer, one asks questions such as Why me? Did I do something wrong or not do something right? Did I not pray enough? Read the Word enough? What in the world happened here?

Having been a faith person for most of my life, I would have never anticipated such questions much less the discoveries that resulted, especially regarding an attitude that needed adjustment.

Throughout the years I've wanted passionately to please God. I gave my life to Him at a young age, but because of my upbringing, it was a long time before I got the message that He loves me "just as I am." I could not connect the words "unconditional" and "love" in the same sentence regarding me, even into my young adulthood years. Unconditional love was something I gave my children but not myself. Eventually, grace won out, and at age 27, I finally received and experienced God's logic-defying love.

Thirty-eight years later, when I got real with God during my cancer journey, I realized that along the way I had lost that childlike sense of just being me and being loved. Little by little I had slipped back into a performance-based syndrome, an easy trap with a slow spring and an iron jaw.

> I had lost that childlike sense of just being me and being loved. Little by little I had slipped back into a performance-based syndrome, an easy trap with a slow spring and an iron jaw.

Unfortunately, believing that relational acceptance depends upon meeting certain expectations robs a person of self-acceptance, too. During that morning, I was once again reminded of how pure, uncomplicated, and beautiful God's love is, as well as how valuable I am to Him. He's not a far-away Deity just waiting for me to mess up. Rather, He's everything I've ever needed or wanted, completely unselfish, and always as close as my next breath. There isn't anyone more enjoyable to me. I do love God.

How does this specifically translate for you? Of course, that's something you have the privilege of finding. My part, I hope, is to inspire you to evaluate for yourself how you see God and discover spiritual peace in your cancer journey.

There's freedom on the other side of getting real with God.

Myth #16: Somehow I've failed spiritually to be facing cancer now. What did I do wrong?

Truth #16: Cancer and shame are not in God's love repertoire, but mercy and compassion are. By His grace, I'm His child and belong to Him. I am flawlessly loved and eternally safe in His care.

Practical Applications

1. I will take time to discover and explore my true emotions regarding cancer.
2. I will give God credit for being good and merciful. I will trust Him with all of my thoughts and feelings, understanding that He is not ashamed of me. Rather, He is my biggest (literally) Supporter and Friend.
3. I will embrace this opportunity to grow in my faith and relationship with God.

Survivor Attitude

I will trust God enough to be real with Him, knowing that His grace (His joyous, non-shaming love power) will enlighten my soul and strengthen my heart. I do not have to live or die in the grips of fear. I can let go of my whole being, past, present, and future to God's care.

CHAPTER SIX

Step #6: Getting Real with the Treatment Process

Cancer Treatment is Hard Work—Be Creative

Preparing for Surgery

On my porch hangs a plaque that I bought before cancer. Admittedly, although I liked the Scripture, I bought it mainly for the color and size, unaware how significant it would become. The Scripture from Romans 15:13 says, "May the God of your hope so fill you with all joy and peace in believing through the experience of your faith that by the power of the Holy Spirit, you may abound and be overflowing with hope." (AMPC)

Wow! That Scripture verse is a perfect prayer for a cancer patient. Joy, peace, faith, the power of God's Spirit, and overflowing hope—I longed for all of those blessings. Hope would surely be the key to success. I was amazed how God strategically placed that plaque in front of me ahead of time, not only for my treatment but also for the duration of my life on this earth.

Hope is like an archer with a quiver full of arrows. I had faith to believe for the target, but I needed hope to help me aim. Without hope, faith has nowhere to go, no way to launch, no direction toward which to land. For me, that was most apparent on the day of surgery and throughout radiation.

> Hope is like an archer with a quiver full of arrows.
> I had faith to believe for the target, but I needed hope
> to help me aim.

"Surgery." The word alone grabbed all sorts of emotions and memories. I had to let go of negative concerns about surgeries and how they can go terribly wrong.

For example, I remembered my dad's triple bypass, how fragile and bluish he looked afterward and the shocking phone call that he was back in surgery for internal bleeding.

I also remembered Shannon undergoing dermabrasion as a 16-year-old after a car accident had left her with glass shard embedded in her forehead. When she emerged from the procedure, her face looked like raw hamburger. I gasped, caught my breath for her sake, and thereafter cared for a young teenage girl living a nightmare.

As a child, I had my first surgery at age 11 months and then again at age two. In those days, treatment for amblyopia ("lazy eye") was in the pioneer stage. From what I understand, I was restrained in bed for 30 days with my eye patched. Of course, I don't consciously remember these things, but when I had a follow-up procedure at age 24, I had a strange sensory connection in that I thought I smelled ether, which was no longer used. Obviously, somehow my childhood surgeries had imprinted their mark on my subconscious mind, so much so that I could reproduce a scent that wasn't there.

In any case, surgery is a big deal, whatever it is and whenever it happens, affecting us on many levels. It's easy to imagine what could go wrong. At first, I tried not to think about such things, but that didn't concur with my getting-real philosophy. On the other hand, I did not want to set myself up for surgical anxiety either. So, how could I begin treatment with peace of mind?

> In any case, surgery is a big deal, whatever it is and whenever it happens, affecting us on many levels. It's easy to imagine what could go wrong.

Although a lumpectomy was not as daunting as a mastectomy, a final selection was problematic. At our clinic, they required a firm, non-revocable decision prior to surgery, which meant that I had to select one or the other in advance, no matter what the pathologist found during the procedure. I couldn't prearrange to switch to a mastectomy if the cancer proved to be regional (spread through the first "sentinel" lymph node.) Or, conversely, if the cancer was localized (in the breast only), I couldn't prearrange to switch to a lumpectomy. That policy, although understandable, complicated my evaluations.

As a result, I requested a lumpectomy but not a conservative one. Specifically, I asked the surgeon to remove a substantial margin of the surrounding tissue, plus some, to ensure that we would eliminate all of the cancer. Absent of fear (see chapter five), I chose this option because the tumor was small, slow growing, and hormone receptor positive with a HER2-negative protein status—all favorable factors for a lumpectomy. We would not be certain of staging until after the surgery, but I had a good chance for stage I cancer. Thank God I had the mammogram that year.

To navigate the day, I deliberately steered it in the direction I wanted. Once I was asleep, I would have no ability to choose, so I planned the things I could choose—the day and time, the type of surgery, and whether I wanted the radioactive tumor locator implanted the evening prior or in the morning. The latter was an easy selection. I couldn't imagine sleeping restfully with a radioactive implant, no matter the size. To give myself something relaxing to do in the morning, I asked Tom to take a walk with me before leaving for the hospital. That felt wonderful. My neighbors were surprised to see me out and about, but I enjoyed seeing them briefly as well.

Little things count. I looked for actions and decisions that would encourage me and help me feel normal.

Little things count. I looked for actions and decisions that would encourage me and help me feel normal.

Myth #17: Surgery is dangerous and always traumatic.

Truth #17: Granted, surgery is dangerous, but so is untreated cancer. As for trauma, I can choose options and plan in such a way that I maximize my safety and success. With forethought and common sense, I can prepare myself for as positive an experience as possible.

Handling the Day of Surgery

Sheila came up from Missouri, and she was finally able to hug me. I closed my eyes and enjoyed her embrace. You know when you're being genuinely loved on. Finally, she was able to participate in person. Shannon had been able to stand shoulder to shoulder with me, but Sheila had the frustration of miles separating us. At last she had arrived, and although in her heart she had been with me all along, she was visibly focused, relieved, and intent on the task ahead. The team of Tom, Marianne, Sheila and Shannon was all under one roof now. Any mom knows that nothing compares with having her loved ones together, whether it's for a holiday dinner, vacation, wedding, birthday, graduation, or sometimes, unfortunately, but perhaps especially, a crisis.

There we were, small but mighty, united and determined. Hope stood in our midst, quiver brimming with arrows. I didn't stop to analyze it at the time, but I know now that all those prayers, discussions, and decisions had culminated to this one all-important day. I was content to let my heart relax and press forward through the surgery. On the way to the hospital I told my family that the hospital only allows two people in the surgical waiting area, but I wanted all three of them there. "I'll find a way" was all over Shannon's face as she responded, "Don't worry about it, Mom. We'll work it out." I smiled, because she negotiates for a living, and I figured that somehow all of my family would be with me.

After receiving my implant and checking in at the surgical desk, the four of us went to the chapel and waited, praying together one more time. When I was summoned, a volunteer began to usher me to the surgical area. The admissions person indicated that I would be going alone and two family members could join me later, so I started to hug everyone. Shannon said, "Just a minute." As I waited nearby, she asked if one of them could come up with me prior to the surgery. When the woman said the room was too small, Shannon responded, "I'm a small person, and I don't take up much room." For my part, I indicated I would like to have someone with me, and in the end, Shannon accompanied me. Since my surgeon's previous procedure was running overtime, I was especially glad to have her company as I waited almost two hours.

After the IV insertion and we were talking with the anesthesiologist, Shannon asked him if her dad and sister could come up. He said, "I don't know why not." And, long story short, even though a nurse protested, both Tom and Sheila joined us. Much to my delight and amusement, Shannon had found a way.

Throughout the day we felt support from relatives and friends. Posts on the MyLifeLine website showed us that they, too, were "overflowing" with hope and ready to believe through the experience of our faith together.

Myth #18: Cancer treatment is a necessary evil.

Truth #18: Cancer treatment is an opportunity to live. I cannot predict or control the treatment, much less the outcome, but at least I have a chance to beat this disease, thanks to the medical advancements and the good people who dedicate their lives to saving ours. I can approach treatment with hope, faith, and gratitude. I am not just enduring the treatment process. I am living it out intentionally.

Healing and Humor in Recovery

When I awoke in recovery, my first remembered thoughts were *I'm alive. I must be okay. Oh, thank God!* As I looked around, a nurse was standing at a machine monitoring me. I said "Hello," and she responded warmly, continuing to check all the instruments. Still groggy, with limited mental filters in operation, I said, "I really like you." I can't explain it other than I felt a little drunk. Laughing softly, she said, "I really like you, too." Then I added, "Thank you for what you do. Isn't it wonderful to know that you are helping God do His work?"

With that, she stopped everything, faced me squarely with a smile that brightened the whole room and said, "Yes, it is." I think we both felt special at that moment.

I've written this section to tell you that, despite the gravity of surgical treatment, you can diminish your concerns by preparing your heart and circumstances carefully. We even had some humorous moments, as shown in the following web post:

"I want to share some lighter moments of the journey. Of course, you know that the McDonoughs can't do anything, even this, without some humor along the way.

On the morning of the surgery, I grabbed a small paper bag to carry my eyeglasses case and ID, the only personal items allowed in the surgery area. Mint green and fairly pretty, the bag was just the right size with a convenient little rope handle. *Perfect,* I thought, but when we got to the Jane Brattain center for the radioactive seed implant (to designate the tumor for the surgeon), Sheila asked me, "Mom, are you sure you want to cart that bag around all day?" My first thought was, *sure, it's small and convenient.* Then I read the outside. It was a Caribou coffee bag saying, "Life is short. Stay awake for it.®" Yikes! Needless to say, the bag was immediately replaced as Sheila made a quick trip to the gift shop, but it was good to start the day with momentary amusement...

While I was recovering at home on Thursday, Sheila and Shannon went to the grocery store, and I decided to sit on the porch. A hospital nurse had given me a fabulous tip to rest my left arm on a pillow for comfort, so I asked Tom to get a pillow, which he was glad to do. He brought it in, and as I lifted my arm, he jammed the pillow into my left side to make sure it wouldn't slip. Good goal but bad idea! After I started breathing again, I saw his penitent face and realized he was really trying to help. Smiling, I looked over my right shoulder and shouted as though the girls could hear me at the grocery store, "Hurry back! Please!" We had a good laugh, and I was fine."

A little humor helped relax me, as did anything we could do to be our normal selves together, from a short walk to a game of cribbage or a mocha latte for a treat.

Myth #19: I won't be able to do anything I normally can or would want to do.

Truth #19: I can be who I am and look for opportunities to be creative and even enjoy humor along the way.

Last But Not Least

At this point, I want to share with you that I am well aware the surgery would have been much more difficult with a mastectomy, the subsequent drainage, and follow-up procedures. I also thank

God that early detection saved me from needing chemotherapy. But those of us who choose the lumpectomy route are required to undergo something mastectomy patients usually don't have to do—radiation, which is a nerve-racking process that lasts almost seven weeks. Radiation was a lot harder than the surgery for me, and, frankly, I can't recall any light moments, much less humor.

Prior to surgery selection, I searched the Internet regarding radiation treatments. Much to my dismay, with each click on a web page, I saw one doom-and-gloom scenario after another. Scorched skin, "weeping" flesh, heart or lung damage, future threats of cancer—lots of depressing stories filled the screen. Plus, medical professionals in the clinic and our family, as delicately as possible, described the dismal hazards. Radiation was my most formidable deterrent to selecting a lumpectomy, but, ultimately, I chose the lumpectomy anyway, knowing that I would have to face radiation.

Radiation is administered every weekday for 6½ weeks, Monday through Friday. It ends up being almost seven weeks, because I had to receive preparation and simulation first. For me, my standing appointment was 10:20 a.m.

On the first day I fumbled through the locker routine, donning the one-size-fits-all mint green robe that hung on my 117-pound frame like a drape on a toaster. I emerged to the waiting room, fingering Bobbie's prayer shawl, which I soon realized matched the robe in the same shade of green. I recalled her words, "Green is for new life," she told me. "And that's what I'm believing for you."

As I entered the radiation room I was surprised at the immensity of the machine. A huge tilting circle of steel with a curving base, similar to the size of an MRI machine, commanded my immediate attention. Shaped like a mammoth portable phone receiver standing upright, the base sloped upward toward an overhanging cylinder with a screen facing downward. Prominently situated in the middle of the base, another screen mirrored the room. Of course, I had no idea which thing did what, but I surmised the circular overhead instrument would administer the radiation. With the machine behind me, I lay on a narrow table that felt like concrete. Above me, photographs of fall and spring leaves decorated the ceiling. Since I love the fall season with its rusty oranges and yellows, I appreciated the pleasant visual.

The technicians hovered as the doctor and physicists determined the technical aspects, dosage, and angles of my treatment. To facilitate exact placement for the beams at subsequent treatments, the doctor tattooed both breasts, a permanent memorial of the experience. Somehow that felt awkward to me, even though the tattoos were tiny dots. It wasn't about the size. It was about the permanence. I knew the tattoos were trivial in the scheme of things, but, logical or not, I felt strangely sad.

Eventually, I learned the drill. Each day I lay on the table in the exact same spot and meticulously positioned myself, lifting my left arm overhead to expose my breasts and left lymph node area. Then I braced my muscles to complete stillness to avoid drawing radiation somewhere it's not supposed to be. I found that my waistband worked well as an anchor for my right hand, fingers entwined in Bobbie's prayer shawl, draped across my lap and reminding me of loving prayers. One day a few weeks into treatment, I inadvertently left my shawl in the car. The technicians patiently waited as I trucked out to the car in my robe to get my shawl.

All of the technicians treated me with compassion, but despite that care, my overarching adjective for radiation is "lonely." After

66

they checked to make sure everything looked right, they walked out, leaving me to the power of the rotating steel umbrella. Behind them, an 18-inch thick door closed like a bank vault. The controls and monitors were in an exterior room. As I lay there, even though clothed everywhere but my chest, I felt fully naked and exposed, with no shielding or protective aprons anywhere. I couldn't help wondering how safe the rest of me was. Sure, the beams targeted my breast, but when it was all said and done, the technicians left the room to protect themselves, and I alone remained. I likened it to having an elephant in the room, and even it left.

> When it was all said and done, the technicians left the room to protect themselves, and I alone remained. I likened it to having an elephant in the room, and even it left.

For sanity's sake, I had to shove those thoughts out of my mind. After the barrier shut and all was quiet, the tilting machine revolved around me, clicking as it went about its duty to kill my cells. It didn't care who I was or that I was a living, breathing human being. It just did its job, namely to destroy everything in its path. Once again, I felt powerless.

Thankfully, the actual treatment was only a few minutes. At first, I tried to pray, but my mind scattered its concerns in hopeless disarray, like litter out of a speeding car. Meanwhile, the ominous duet of silence and clicking delivered its precise, unalterable performance. I shut my eyes, which only increased my isolation. What could I do? I had to counteract the sense of vulnerability that besieged me and reflected the dutiful restraint of my body.

On the way home, I managed to pinpoint the issue. I had to select a powerful and memorable mental diversion. Recalling Matt Redman's song, "10,000 Reasons," one of the songs that inspired me just prior to diagnosis, I turned to Psalm 103, the Scripture upon which "10,000 Reasons" is based:

> ¹ Bless the Lord, O my soul;
> And all that is within me, bless His holy name!
> ² Bless the Lord, O my soul,
> And forget not all His benefits:
> ³ Who forgives all your iniquities,
> Who heals all your disease,
> ⁴ Who redeems your life from destruction,
> Who crowns you with lovingkindness and tender mercies,
> ⁵ Who satisfies your mouth with good things,
> So that your youth is renewed like the eagle's. (NKJV)

As I read it, sang, and reread it, that extraordinary Scripture began a faithful vigil that continues to this day. I knew, just as surely as I've ever known anything, that God's Word could and would help me handle the radiation regimen.

Excited, I determined to memorize and then meditate on Psalm 103:1-5 during the radiation. My plan was to select a different Scripture for each week. I felt encouraged to have a plan, any plan at all, much less such a good one.

As I lay there the second day of radiation, I closed my eyes and slowly prayed Psalm 103:1-5 in my heart, repeating it about five to six times. The clicking droned on, but it seemed to be more of a backdrop than center stage. Amazingly, my mind wasn't in charge of the situation any more. God's Word trumped the circumstances, the anxiety diminished, and I didn't feel alone and vulnerable any more.

All week Psalm 103:1-5 was more than enough for me, and by the second week, to my surprise, I had no interest in finding another Scripture.

Then during the third, fourth, fifth, even through the "boost" period when they increased the dosage at the end, I could not get enough of Psalm 103. As it turned out, those five verses were strong enough to carry me through every day of every week for the whole regimen!

Did I still feel some anxiety? Of course. Despite my best efforts, I had some moments. But the Word, Christ Himself, was my Companion. He bunkered inside the radiation room with me where no one else could stand the battle. The 18-inch door did not stop Him. Danger did not deter Him. Cancer could not defeat Him.

> But the Word, Christ Himself, was my companion.
> He bunkered inside the radiation room with me where no one else could stand the battle. The 18-inch door did not stop Him. Danger did not deter Him.
> Cancer could not defeat Him.

He walked with me in the valley of the shadow of death.

To this day, at 10:20 a.m. my cell phone alarm reminds me to thank God I don't have cancer and meditate on Psalm 103:1-5. I still love that Scripture and have never tired of it.

I write this section to help breast cancer patients understand that the lumpectomy/radiation route, when considered in its entirety, is a precarious journey, too. I once heard a celebrity talk about her lumpectomy and radiation. She said it was "no big deal." I disagree, and I don't want women whose staging allows them the less radical treatment to have their experience invalidated as trivial. Please don't let anyone do that to you!

Any cancer is a crisis at any level with any treatment protocol. Moreover, respect is due to all of us who conquer our fears and find the power to fight this heinous disease, no matter the regimen or outcome.

Stand tall, cancer warrior!

Myth #20: During the actual treatment, away from family and friends, I am utterly alone.

Truth #20: Someone, an unlimited Someone, is with me wherever I am, and His presence will take me through anything.

Practical Applications

1. I will arrange my treatment schedule in such a way that I minimize stress and maximize recovery.
2. I will search for creative ways to undergo treatment in such a way that I feel confident and safe.
3. I will intentionally plan activities that feel normal to me.
4. I will communicate with my family and/or support people ahead of time to avoid surprises and facilitate the treatment.

Survivor Attitude

I will approach cancer treatment as an opportunity to live. With determination, I will plan each day intentionally, do everything I can to maximize the effectiveness of my treatment, and find ways to incorporate humor and laughter. I will never be the same, but that is a good thing. I will appreciate life more as a survivor.

CHAPTER SEVEN

Step #7: Getting Real with Stress

Cancer Causes Stress—Use It to Your Advantage

When Everything Seems to Go Wrong

Think about stress you've experienced, not only in cancer but also in your daily life. Stress happens to all of us, and it can do a lot of damage. Countless books, news reports, magazine articles, scientific studies, television shows, and all sorts of media plead a case against stress in our lives, because it can make us sick in body, soul, and spirit.

Let's face facts. Bad things happen along the way for all of us. I don't know anyone on life's transit who gets a free pass from unscheduled stops, accidents, and delays. In and of themselves, such things are not inherently stress, per se. Stress is our reaction to life's difficulties, and that is what I want to address in this chapter regarding stress in the cancer journey.

Have you ever heard the statement, "When it rains, it pours"? I'd love to tell you that it's nothing but an old adage, but my cancer experience got us pretty darn wet—literally.

The following all happened within the three-month period from mammogram through radiation:

- Day after biopsy: Tom's car was rear ended. Fortunately, he wasn't hurt.

- First week of radiation: Someone stole Tom's trailer (worth $20,000) from his parking lot at work. Even with surveillance camera footage, the police didn't get a good enough image of the truck license plate to catch the guy.

- Second week of radiation: On the first radiation day that I drove myself, I decided afterward to stop at a local sandwich shop and treat myself. As I was leaving the parking lot, another car and I collided in a fender bender. Although upset, I was not hurt.

- Third week of radiation: My office flooded with a sewage backup almost two feet deep on Tuesday afternoon. Wednesday, after radiation, Tom and I donned boots and rubber gloves to salvage as much as possible. We ended up disposing most of it. I grieved the loss of furniture, file cabinets, books, resources, and documents drenched with foul water and therefore non-salvageable.

- Fifth week of radiation: A water pipe burst in the ceiling of a bedroom in the lower level of our home, saturating the ceiling, walls, furniture, carpet, and closet, as well as part of the carpet in the family room. I was about to start the most intense part of radiation, the "boost" period with increased dosage concentration. As we stood in the middle of the bedroom, water squishing beneath our feet again (at least it was clean this time), Tom and I started to laugh. Yes, we actually laughed. "What's a little water?" I said. "Doesn't bother me," he said. We high-fived and went to work.

Many times I've seen people go through crises, only to have more mishaps, accidents, and even traumas crescendo through stress-burdened days like dominoes in a straight-line wind. Unfortunately, my experience took the same route, and I imagine theories abound to explain that. In any case, I learned a few things about stress under cancer fire.

First of all, getting real helps disarm the stress. After my car accident, I managed to remain fairly calm but I was truly upset and communicated that fact quite well to both the other driver and my insurance agent. I even shared that I was undergoing radiation. Similarly, the loss of my office hit me hard at the time. As Tom and I waded through sewer water, I felt sad and frustrated, but Tom had worked in the sewers of Chicago as a teenager, and it didn't bother him the way it did me. We were good problem solvers together that day.

So, how does getting real disarm stress? When truth emerges, we avoid the pseudo-stoicism that keeps the incident in control of us. As we speak honestly, releasing our thoughts and emotions, we disarm the power of the problem and invite creativity.

> When truth emerges, we avoid the pseudo-stoicism that keeps the incident in control of us.

Moreover, getting real helps us put stress in its proper place. Compared to cancer, car accidents and floods registered low on the stress scale, as evidenced by our response. Thankfully, the second flooding failed to overwhelm us.

Finally, getting real helps us identify the stress for what it is and move toward a greater good. I liken stress to looking through a kaleidoscope. As we twist the barrel, an orderly design tumbles into temporary disarray, but when the chips settle, a rearranged design displays a new beauty, just as good, if not better than the former one. Although we notice the scrambled chips, we anticipate a glorious result.

Thus, if we don't succumb to stress, identify the truth of the situation, and trust God, we can find a greater good for our lives.

Applying the kaleidoscope theory, I enjoyed extraordinary designs:

- Neither Tom nor I were injured or had any after-effects from the car mishaps. I decided to trade my car in for one with better visibility, got a great deal, and loved my new car.

- Because of surveillance footage, Tom got the full $20,000 from his insurance.

- The sewer backup rendered my office space unusable, such that I could not longer lease there, but I found a much better office, not in a lower level, and only five minutes from home.

- The loss of property and documents taught me a valuable lesson on document storage and maintenance.

- Our next-door neighbor had just started dating a man who did estimates for a water damage company. He came over and guided us through the whole process, which enabled us to remodel the whole bedroom and transform it into a more teenage-friendly space for my granddaughters who were fast losing interest in the princess/stuffed animal décor anyway.

As it turned out, our insurance companies helped us minimize expenses, the kaleidoscope chips settled, and I was surprised by unanticipated blessings.

Myth #21: Stress always depletes and destroys.

Truth #21: Stress is a gateway to change. We can use it to redesign our lives for a better good.

Don't Ever Give Up

How many stories have your heard about people who persevered through the toughest times but found a breakthrough just around the bend? Certainly, the cancer journey is no exception.

You may recall that when I got real with God, I talked about books, ministry projects, and exciting visions to pursue. During the first few weeks of cancer, those goals seemed far away. After surgery, to my relief, I gradually resumed a more normal schedule despite the daily morning radiation regimen. Because I want to help you, however, I have to share that I was tired, not weaker necessarily or incapacitated, but I could feel a definite difference. The treatment process in its entirety, especially radiation, took a temporary toll on my physical endurance and energy. Fortunately, I discovered that short, intermittent walks and sensible nutrition helped a lot, but I needed time to heal.

After radiation in June, I scrambled to finish preparations for a July seminar planned for my visual artists network. Since I had previously arranged a fabulous speaker and location, I kept the project on the calendar, even though the timing was tenuous.

Great Commission Artists was in its inaugural year, a critical stage for any organization. I refused to jeopardize the momentum gained from our kickoff event in March.

More concerning was our biggest project of the year, our first *Psalms Exhibit and Creative Arts Celebration* slated for September. Since I had not designed or organized an art exhibit before, I had a large learning curve to surmount. Meanwhile, I also devoted energy to other miscellaneous writing and ministry commitments that had been put on hold.

After Waterfalls, the seminar in July, I dragged myself home as tired as I've ever been, but it was beautiful. Gratefully, I can report that Great Commission Artists was launched successfully. Now I'm glad I got over the hump that seemed more like Mount Everest at the time.

In this mix of events, I did get a wonderful treat. Tom and I had scheduled a special family trip to Ireland to celebrate our 45th anniversary. My challenge, however, was to get the *Psalms Exhibit* business and registration in gear before leaving in August. As it turned out, the trip was amazing and more than worth the extra effort to make it happen.

By the end of 2012, my to-do list still had some stragglers, but overall I felt good about the year. Just as I am grateful for the mammogram I didn't cancel, I am equally glad that I didn't give up my goals because cancer invaded my life.

At this point in your own process, the thought of work responsibilities and goals may seem overwhelming. Depending on your situation, the stress can be brutal. I understand, but please keep this in mind: your number one task is to heal. We'll talk about the future in the next chapter.

Myth #22: I've lost so much time and energy, all I can do now is exist.

Truth #22: I may have to adjust my life for physical changes, but I can follow through with my plans as best I can. I would rather give myself the opportunity to succeed than give up and miss a potential victory.

Cancer Changes Perspective

Cancer changed my perspective on life occurrences. Do I get stressed now and then? Surely, but I handle many things differently now, and I feel more in tune with myself, hearing hope's melody and choreographing my faith to the sound.

> I handle many things differently now, and I feel more in tune with myself, hearing hope's melody and choreographing my faith to the sound.

Cancer also changed my perspective on people. I feel more connected and alive. Whenever someone asks me, "How are you?" my answer is easy. I know they don't want to say, "How's the cancer?" so I imitate Mike Lubratovich and answer the question behind the question. Gratefully, I say something like, "I'm doing well. Thanks for asking," or "I just had my check-up, and everything looks good." How lovely it is that people still care and pray for me!

Tom has a buddy named Bob Ward, the husband of a woman who used to be in a worship group I led. When I was diagnosed,

Bob committed to pray for me daily at 11:11 a.m. When he told Tom that he felt God led him to do that, Tom decided to join in. Since then, every morning, 11:11 a.m., my husband's cell phone alerts him to pray. I assure you, I love hearing that lovely little melody whenever I'm within earshot.

Cancer also changed my perspective on myself, certainly an unexpected benefit. Armed with truth, a great support team, and God's grace, I found the power to confront cancer and move forward. Despite faltering now and then, I attacked it hard and managed to keep my commitments and goals. Now I'm proud of the way I navigated this vicious disease.

I've shared my story to help you choose how you want to face cancer. You might falter now and then, too, but that's all right. Wherever you are on your journey, especially if you've just been diagnosed, you can overcome the stress and come out stronger.

It's totally worth it.

Myth #23: Having had cancer means I'm weaker, less whole, and impaired for the rest of my life.

Truth #23: I fought hard, and I'm still here. I can welcome the changes in my life, share my experiences, and help other cancer warriors coming up behind me.

Practical Applications

1. I will trust God to work everything for my ultimate good.
2. I will carefully evaluate important commitments going forward, and when wisdom concurs, I will continue to pursue my passions and goals.
3. I will embrace my new and improved perspectives and relationships.

Survivor Attitude

I will not lose heart. If I lose that, what do I have left? I will use stress as a gateway to change. No matter what happens, I can apply the kaleidoscope theory and find a new design for my life.

CHAPTER EIGHT

Step #8: Getting Real with Your Future
Life After Cancer—Be Vigilant and Celebrate

No Illusions

Life after cancer isn't easy, and I would be remiss to claim otherwise. Did I grow as a person during cancer treatment? Absolutely. Did I make positive changes and develop survivor attitudes? Yes, and I'm glad for each one. But I want to be clear: getting through cancer and life thereafter requires a pit-bull grip on your health care goals.

> I want to be clear: getting through cancer and life thereafter requires a pit-bull grip on your health care goals.

First, I had to grieve the loss of what I call "life innocence." Prior to cancer, I didn't give a serious thought to the words "terminal" or "death" with respect to my own life. In a way, I had a childlike, carefree innocence, pursuing my daily activities and goals as though I would be here forever. Today I realize how lovely that innocence was, despite its lack of reality, and wish I had appreciated it. Breast exams have changed from a precautionary practice to a regimen, and I can't nonchalantly disregard a bump anywhere on my body as just a bump.

As you can well imagine by now, I am a proud proponent of "mamms." Please, whether you're a cancer patient, a friend, or a relative, I urge you to get your mammograms annually or any cancer screening advised for you. As you may recall, I could have skipped my mammogram in 2012. Thank God, I did not!

Since that time I've been faithful to monitor my health. Having experienced cancer's shadow, I don't want to get in its vicinity again.

Consequently, I offer you some straight cancer talk, because if I don't and you struggle somehow, you could think there's something wrong with you. Cancer survival is a way of life, an ongoing process within a continuum of constant learning, vigilance, and courage.

Whatever our faith, we all experience problems at times. For my life, I recall the words of Christ, "In this world you will have trouble. But take heart. I have overcome the world." (John 16:33, NIV) He didn't say if we do everything right, we won't have any more problems, or if we're good people, we'll be exempt from anything bad interrupting our plans. Instead, the reality is that life has trials, but I love the phrase, "take heart." Taking heart can seem impossible when we're frustrated, but the rewards are life changing.

Along the way we may become discouraged or disheartened. After all, crisis and even relapse happens sometimes, as hard as that is to understand. No matter the scenario, however, we cannot stop hoping, for hope is the cradle of vision. Rather, we disengage from the anxiety of trying to control our tomorrows. In fact, getting real with the future requires letting go of it. If we can do that, anxiety can't hold us captive in the dark tunnel of fear where despair suffocates hope.

Getting real with the future requires letting go of it.

Thankfully, by the time I reached the other side of treatment, I found the warrior inside of me, not a fearless woman, but a grace-dependent one who could face fear and overcome. Parts of the old me had to give way, but I am still Marianne, maybe even more childlike in some ways and definitely more purposeful. I rejoice in what I've learned and welcome additions to the new me—a stronger person, more determined and grateful for each new day.

Now I've written a book to encourage you, wherever you are in your cancer journey, to move forward, above where you've been, and perhaps far beyond where you've dared to dream. When adversity interferes or threatens you, hold on to what you know to be true and persevere.

You can move forward, above where you've been,
and perhaps far beyond where you've dared to dream.
When adversity interferes or threatens you,
hold on to what you know to be true and persevere.

Treasure your life, every beautiful breath of it.

Myth #24: If I encounter problems or setbacks, there's something wrong with me.

Truth #24: Problems or setbacks are part of life. I am not alone in that regard. I can take heart and persevere.

Celebrate Anniversaries

Approximately one year after diagnosis, on March 3, 2013, not even thinking about my cancer journey, I went to church with Tom for the mid-morning service. To my delight, the worship opened with "You Never Let Go" delivered by a full orchestra and a choir of at least 40 enthusiastic singers. Immediately, as they began the song that had so inspired me one year earlier, I remembered my upcoming anniversary. Closing my eyes, I relished the sound and decided "You Never Let Go" had never been more beautiful. Although God multitasks better than anyone, surely intending the music to minister to the whole congregation, I felt as though He had sent me a special anniversary present.

But that wasn't all that happened.

"You Never Let Go" was followed by "10,000 Reasons." How amazing is that? Especially considering that the worship leader had no knowledge of my personal story or the significance of those two songs paired together on that day. If that were not enough, the next week, at our other church at the cabin, the worship team there sang "10,000 Reasons." Astonished, I couldn't help but feel that my anniversary was well worth celebrating.

Since then, I've learned with each passing year that surviving cancer is one of the best things that ever happened to me.

Myth #25: My future is limited.

Truth #25: My future is an ongoing opportunity to create and design my life.

Two years after treatment, on my second anniversary in March 2014, again I arrived at Sunday service at our home church with no thoughts about the two-year mark. This time our new worship pastor selected "10,000 Reasons" for that morning.

Now, I realize it's a popular song, but think about it. Three different worship leaders, with hundreds of options, chose "10,000 Reasons" exactly on time for my cancer journey and anniversaries three years in a row. I'm not a mathematician, so I can't calculate those odds, but odds are irrelevant when God is involved.

This year, during a February trip to Missouri, the worship leader in Sheila's church sang "10,000 Reasons." With tears streaming down my face, I turned to my grandchildren and said, "That's my song. That's the song that took me through cancer."

Myth #26: The future is unpredictable and ultimately futile.

Truth #26: Why not believe that God has the power to do more than I can think or imagine for my future?

I Still Need My Support Team

We all have tender spots in our souls. For my generation, those tender spots are called "grandchildren."

January 1, 2014, spun us into another crisis as our youngest granddaughter, Daisy (8 years old at the time), had to be hospitalized for type 1 diabetes. She was slated for treatment when they returned to Missouri after their Christmas visit, but, inordinately high blood sugar and ketone levels required emergency care. During the next few days, we learned things we never expected to know, like how to give shots and handle a hypoglycemic emergency. At such times, grandparents' tender spots take quite a hit.

Shortly thereafter I went to Missouri for Daisy's birthday, which was lovely. Although her test levels were still erratic, she was doing quite well. The night before I left I remarked to Lauren, my oldest granddaughter, "Grandpa and I pray every morning for a cure for diabetes." With typical candor, she responded, "Are you also praying for a cure for cancer every day?"

"No."

"Why not, Grandma?"

Of course, Lauren cared about her sister's situation, but she encouraged me to stay engaged in prayer for cancer, too. To this day, I know that Lauren, Natalie, and Daisy, and in fact, all of my family members are faith warriors in my behalf.

Since that time, Tom and I have resumed our prayers for a cure for cancer and protection for myself. Currently, by the way, promising advances in immunotherapy are emerging.

A Word to the Wise

My oncology clinic, in its follow-up instructions, included the following: "As treatment ends, people start to feel better physically. But, ending treatment can trigger a rush of emotions, ranging from excitement and celebration to anger and sadness. This emotional change happens because cancer survivors often relax their guard and process all the feelings they put aside during treatment. . . For many people, this change leads to two to three months of emotional ups and downs."

That precaution confirms everything I've written to you! Do not put all your emotions aside. Getting real not only empowers treatment, but it also prepares you for stronger survivorship.

Myth #27: A cure for cancer is unlikely.

Truth #27: That's how people used to view lots of diseases such as tuberculosis, polio, AIDS, heart attacks, and strokes. Even if medicine were not advancing at its current mind-boggling rate, I believe that researchers can and will discover a cure for cancer.

The Ultimate Truth

As we draw to a close, I encourage you to write a summation of your own beliefs. For me, as a Christian, mine are as follows:

Cancer told me my life was over, but Psalm 103 assured me that God heals.

Cancer told me I would be destroyed, but Psalm 103 said God redeems my life from destruction.

Cancer told me God had forsaken me, but Psalm 103 described me as crowned with loving kindness and tender mercies.

Cancer told me, if I did survive, I wouldn't be capable of living much of a life, but Psalm 103 promised me physical provision and youth renewed like the eagle's.

Bottom line: Cancer is not in charge of my life, and God is. No one tells the truth, the whole truth, and nothing but the truth better than He does.

> Bottom line: Cancer is not in charge of my life, and God is.

Do I know what's going to happen to me next year or subsequently? Of course not! I'm too mortal, too human, and fallible. I can't even predict this afternoon, much less five, ten, or more years from now.

Do I understand why some people survive longer than others? No, I can't do that either. I'm not that smart. Such knowledge far surpasses my finite brain and limited experience. Inexplicable events puzzle me as much as the next person.

Life is fragile and resilient, fleeting and enduring, fast and slow. But, in the final analysis, whatever life is, whatever the journey, one thing is certain: We don't have the ability to be our own god. Many things, especially in the cancer battle, are beyond our capacity to comprehend, much less control. Thus, our hearts cry out for Someone with infinite knowledge and unfettered power Whose love never fails.

Have you seen the science lately? New nebula sprout across the galaxies, displaying the glories of Creator God Who continues to do that which He alone can. When the earth was still formless, empty, and engulfed in darkness, He set His Word in motion, saying, "Let there be Light." Today, nothingness continues to respond to the eternal impact of that Word as fledgling stars emerge. So, I have to ask, is anyone better qualified to handle and direct our lives?

Now add to that concept, the whole matter of grace. God is the only One Who creates and gives grace, a gift of fierce love that monsters like cancer cannot overcome, no matter what happens.

God is the only One Who creates and gives grace,
a gift of fierce love that monsters like cancer
cannot overcome, no matter what happens.

In conclusion and with genuine respect, I feel privileged to have shared my story and thoughts with all of you, especially newly-diagnosed cancer warriors. As we rally against our common enemy, embracing the beliefs we've discerned and treasuring the power therein, I hope we will all be able to say together, "Today we don't have cancer," and celebrate how incredibly wonderful that is!

Practical Applications

1. I will diligently monitor my health and pray for protection.
2. I will open my eyes to everyday blessings.
3. I will rejoice at every anniversary.
4. I will pray for increased prevention awareness and a cure for cancer.
5. I will let go of my future to God.

Survivor Attitude

I will make the most of my future, appreciating how beautiful life is and what a privilege it is to have more time on this earth.

CPSIA information can be obtained
at www.ICGtesting.com
Printed in the USA
LVOW10s2311251016

510290LV00008B/314/P